LAWRENCE HOHMAN

About the Artist/Author

Lawrence (Larry) Hohman has recently finished his first wildlife art project by completing the alphabet with 26 color pencil renderings of various birds.

Born and raised in Cleveland, Ohio, Hohman's talent for drawing was honed at The Cleveland Institute of Art. After graduation, he went to work as an art studio designer, then as an advertising agency art director, and finally as the owner of a commercial art studio. He owned the studio for 26 years, until retiring in 1996.

From buying land on which he built a small log cabin from the trees on the property, to enjoying golf and gardening, Hohman shows a true love of nature and the outdoors. He has four grown daughters and lives in Olmsted Falls, Ohio, with his wife Evelyn.

ISBN 0-9728954-0-X

A is for Albatross
out on the sea,
searching for food
and flying away free.

B is for Blue jay
up in the corn,
gathering his food
in the early morn.

C is for Cardinal
a glowing and bright red,
upon a tasty snail
he soon will have fed.

D is for Ducklings
both fuzzy and soft,
seeking some water
to paddle their way off.

E is for Eagle
swift and so fierce,
with sharp pointy beak
that can and will pierce.

F is for Finch
a bright colorful bird,
while courting his mate
a *tick-tick* can be heard.

G is for Goose
from Canada it came,
seen everywhere now
they all look the same.

H is for Heron
stalking the bog,
looking for food
like a little frog.

I is for Ibis
majestic and white,
with a long curvy beak
he'll catch a meal right.

J is for Junco
by a thistle weed,
drawn to its beauty
and flavory seed.

K is for Kingfisher
with eyes that see all,
and a swift diver too
who's just caught his meal.

L is for the lonely Loon
on a quiet, peaceful lake,
its eerie laughing sound
could cause people to forsake.

M is for Mockingbird
bringing food to the nest,
a fearsome looking dragonfly
that will feed all the rest.

N is for Nuthatch
in among the pines,
searching for seeds
upon which he dines.

O is for Owl
vith its spookish hoot,
on still moonlit nights
rapped in feathery suit.

P is for Puffin
a colorful clown,
burrows its nest
in a secret down.

Q is for Quail
with head-plume over,
can often be found
eating wild red clover.

R is for Robin
pulling hard and firm,
he's the early bird
that gets the worm.

S is for Sparrow
on very top of bush,
its *pit-tuck-zeeeee* song
tells of springtime rush.

T is for Turkey
in a pumpkin patch,
scurrying along
before he's a catch.

U is for Upupa epops
a funny name for a bird,
also known as the Hoopoe
another quite silly word.

V is for Vulture
food-searching for more,
he's truly a bird that
can circle and soar.

W is for Woodpecker
on a hollow tree that,
the sound he can make
is a *rat-a-tat-tat*.

X is for Xantus' murrelet
off southern California's coast,
rarely found more northerly
Baja's where it's seen the most.

Y is for Yellowlegs
whose very obvious feet,
are mistaken for reeds
by the minnows he'll eat.

Z is for Zenaida dove
on the tree inside the yard,
tending to the fertile nest
while also being on his guard.